P9-BJF-283

Eruption

Contents

You can find out about all these things in this book!

Volcanoes

There are volcanoes all around the world.

Some volcanoes will not erupt again.
They are dead or extinct.
You may have read
about some animals that are extinct.
That means that they are all gone
and will not come back again.

Some volcanoes are sleeping.
If a volcano is sleeping,
it is dormant.
It could "wake up" at any time.

Some volcanoes are "awake" or active.
Active volcanoes rumble and grumble,
and they may erupt!

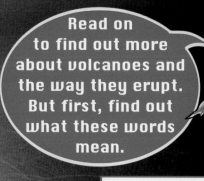

Read on
to find out more
about volcanoes and
the way they erupt.
But first, find out
what these words
mean.

Lava (lah va)
Lava is the red hot rock that
erupts from a volcano.

Magma (mag mah)
Magma is the red hot rock
that lies under the volcano
before it erupts.

Magma chamber
A magma chamber is a place
under the volcano
where magma is held.

The earth's crust
The earth's crust
is like a thin skin –
a skin of rock.

Vent
A vent is an opening
in the earth's crust.

ash and gas and molten rock

What Makes a Volcano Erupt?

The earth is so hot
under an active volcano
that the rock melts,
like snow melts in the sun.
Melted rock is called magma.
A magma chamber
holds the magma.
When a volcano erupts,
the magma comes up
from the chamber.
It comes up and out
through vents
in the earth's crust.

4

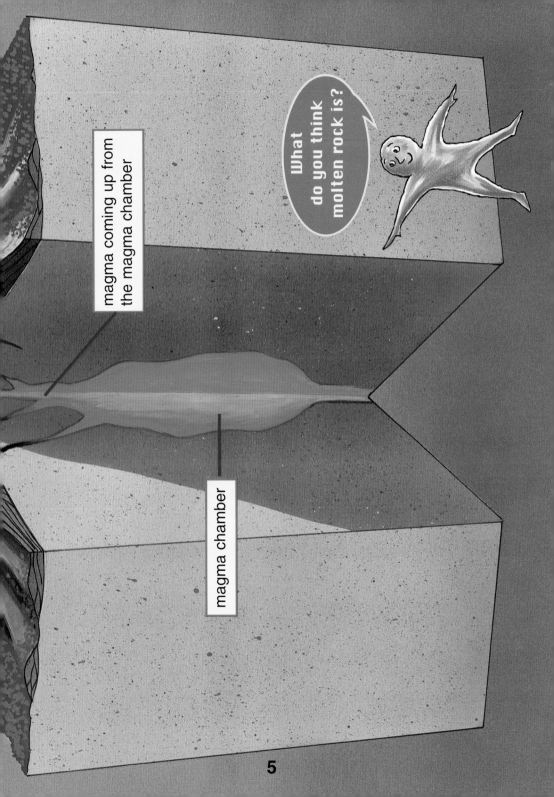

Kinds of Eruptions

You may think
that all volcanoes
erupt in the same way.
But they don't.

Some volcanoes are gentle.
The magma from these volcanoes
comes slowly out of vents
in the earth's crust.

Some volcanoes are strong.
When these volcanoes erupt,
they can kill many people.

Not all volcanic eruptions
are the same.

Can you
see why these
eruptions are not
the same?

This eruption throws
ash, rocks, and gas
high into the air.
It is called a Plinian
(plinee an) eruption.

This eruption throws lava from many vents. It is a Hawaiian eruption.

This eruption blasts gas and molten rock from its vent. It is called a Strombolian (Strombol eean) eruption.

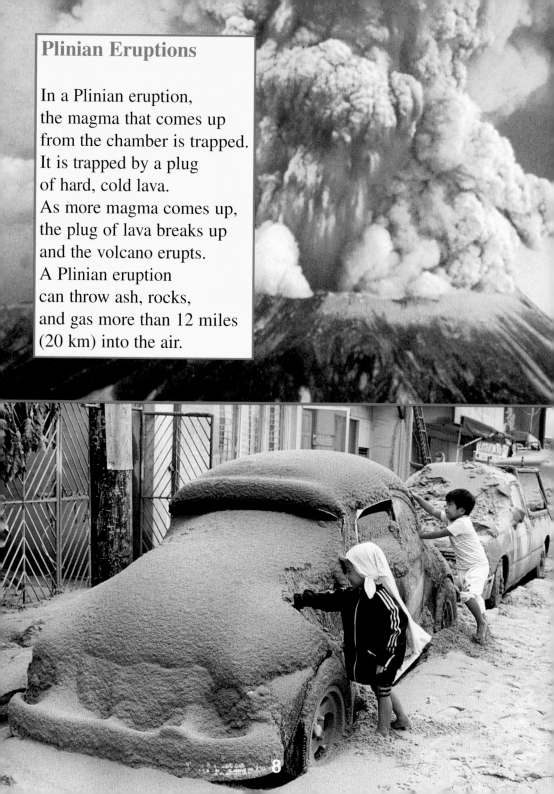

Plinian Eruptions

In a Plinian eruption,
the magma that comes up
from the chamber is trapped.
It is trapped by a plug
of hard, cold lava.
As more magma comes up,
the plug of lava breaks up
and the volcano erupts.
A Plinian eruption
can throw ash, rocks,
and gas more than 12 miles
(20 km) into the air.

Two thousand years ago,
a man named Pliny (Plin ee)
saw a big volcano erupt.
The volcano
was called Mount Vesuvius
(Vuh soo vee us).
It threw ash over the town
of Pompeii (Pom pay),
and it killed
more than 20,000 people.
Pliny wrote
about the eruption
that he had seen.
That is why
this kind of eruption
is called a Plinian eruption.

A person killed
by the ash of
Mount Vesuvius

9

Hawaiian Eruptions

In an Hawaiian eruption,
runny lava spills out of a crater.
The runny lava
can move a long, long way.

The lava that comes
out of the crater is very hot
and may look like fire.
As it moves away
from the volcano,
it kills things that are in its way.
When the lava cools down
and gets cold, it gets hard.

The name "Hawaiian eruption"
was picked because the volcanoes
on the Hawaiian Islands
erupt like this.

Strombolian Eruptions

In a Strombolian eruption,
the magma is not so runny,
and it is full of gases
that are trapped.
As the magma rises,
the gas makes a big blast.
This blast throws lava
high into the air.
When the lava falls,
it cools down
and lands around the vent
of the volcano.
Strombolian volcanoes
end up with very steep sides.

Mt Stromboli gives its name to a Strombolian eruption.

13

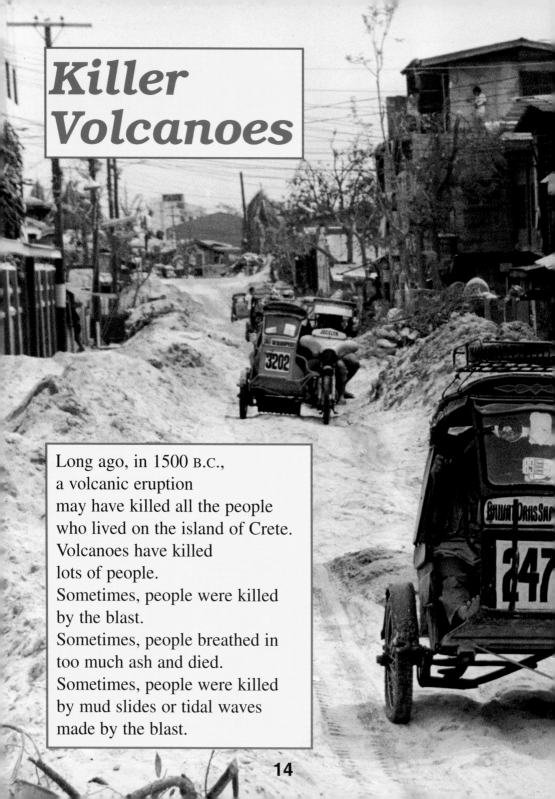

Killer Volcanoes

Long ago, in 1500 B.C.,
a volcanic eruption
may have killed all the people
who lived on the island of Crete.
Volcanoes have killed
lots of people.
Sometimes, people were killed
by the blast.
Sometimes, people breathed in
too much ash and died.
Sometimes, people were killed
by mud slides or tidal waves
made by the blast.

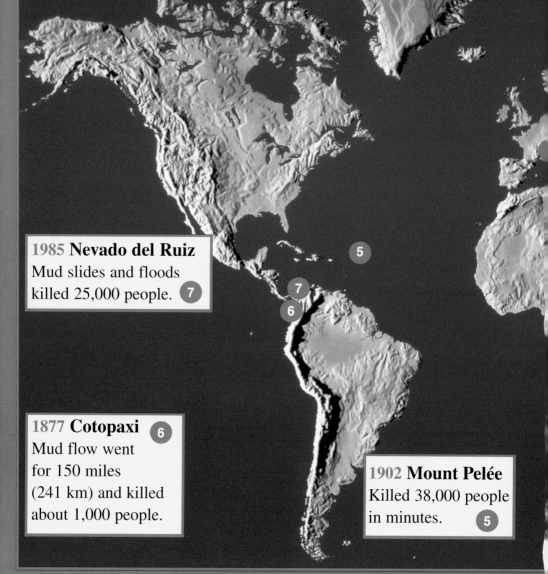

The Killers

1985 Nevado del Ruiz
Mud slides and floods killed 25,000 people. **7**

1877 Cotopaxi **6**
Mud flow went for 150 miles (241 km) and killed about 1,000 people.

1902 Mount Pelée
Killed 38,000 people in minutes. **5**

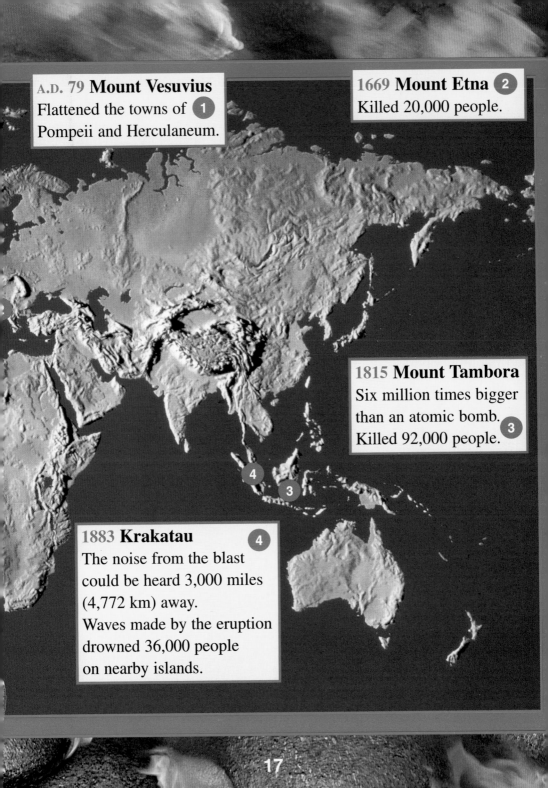

A.D. 79 **Mount Vesuvius**
Flattened the towns of ①
Pompeii and Herculaneum.

1669 **Mount Etna** ②
Killed 20,000 people.

1815 **Mount Tambora**
Six million times bigger
than an atomic bomb. ③
Killed 92,000 people.

1883 **Krakatau** ④
The noise from the blast
could be heard 3,000 miles
(4,772 km) away.
Waves made by the eruption
drowned 36,000 people
on nearby islands.

Escape from Mount Api

Written by Judy Ling
Illustrated by Marjorie Scott

Jose couldn't sleep.
It was a hot night.
He lay in bed.
He thought about his father.
His father had to work in the city
to get money for the family.
Sometimes he was gone so long
that when he came home
he was like a stranger.
Jose often thought
that his father did not love him.

> Why does Jose's room look so red?

Just then Jose heard a rumbling noise.
He got up and looked out his window.
The sky was red.
Then all the dogs in the street howled.
The rumbling noise came again.
Louder and louder.
It came from Mount Api.
Jose was scared.
The old people said
that long ago, Mount Api had erupted.
It had killed many people.
The old people still did not like the mountain.
"You never know what a volcano will do!" they said.

18

The rumbling got louder and louder.
Jose ran to wake up his mother.
"Wake up, wake up!" he called.

"Go to sleep, Jose!" said his mother.
"I am tired. Go back to bed."

"Mount Api is erupting," cried Jose.
"Listen to the rumbling!"

His mother ran to the window.
"You're right, Jose," she said.
"Wake up your sisters.
I'll get our things."

Jose woke up his little sisters.
"Don't cry," he said.
"We must go away fast.
Do as I say and you will be all right."

What sort of things will Jose's family take with them?

20

Jose and his sisters and mother
left the house and ran down the street.
"VOLCANO!" Jose shouted
as they went.

There was red hot lava
all over Mount Api.
A cloud of gas and ash
swirled above the lava.
"We'll be killed!" Jose cried
as they ran in the dark.

Then Jose saw a car.
He pulled at the car door.
"Please take us with you," cried Jose
to the driver.
"Don't let us die!"

"Get in!" said the driver.
Jose and his mother and his sisters
all jumped in the car.

"Let's go," said the driver.

25

The driver went faster and faster,
away from the ash and the gas
that the volcano threw out.
They drove for a long time.
The driver stopped at a small village.
All the lights were on.
The people were in the streets.
They had heard about Mount Api.

"You can get out here," said the driver.
"You'll be safe now."

Some people in the village
took Jose and his mother
and sisters to a school.
They gave them drinks and blankets.

More and more people came.
Some were hurt.
Some had lost their families.
All had lost their homes.

27

The villagers looked after them,
but Jose was worried.
"We can't stay here forever,"
he said to his mother.
"Now that we have lost our home,
how will Dad find us?
How will we pay for food to eat?"

"I'm sure Dad will find us,"
said his mother.

Then, one night,
Jose saw someone at the door.

"Dad!" he shouted. "Dad!"
He threw himself into his father's arms.
His father hugged him.
"My family!" he cried.
"Are you all right?"

Jose's dad hugged
his wife and daughters.
"When I heard about Mount Api,
I took the first plane home," he said.
"I thought you were all dead.
Then I heard that
you were safe,
so I came looking for you."

"Dad," Jose said sadly,
"our home is gone.
We have lost everything.
What will we do?"

"You are all safe," said his father.
"That is all that matters."

And Jose cried…
but not because he was sad.
He knew now
that his father really loved him.

Will Jose and
his family go back
to their old home?

30

31

Index